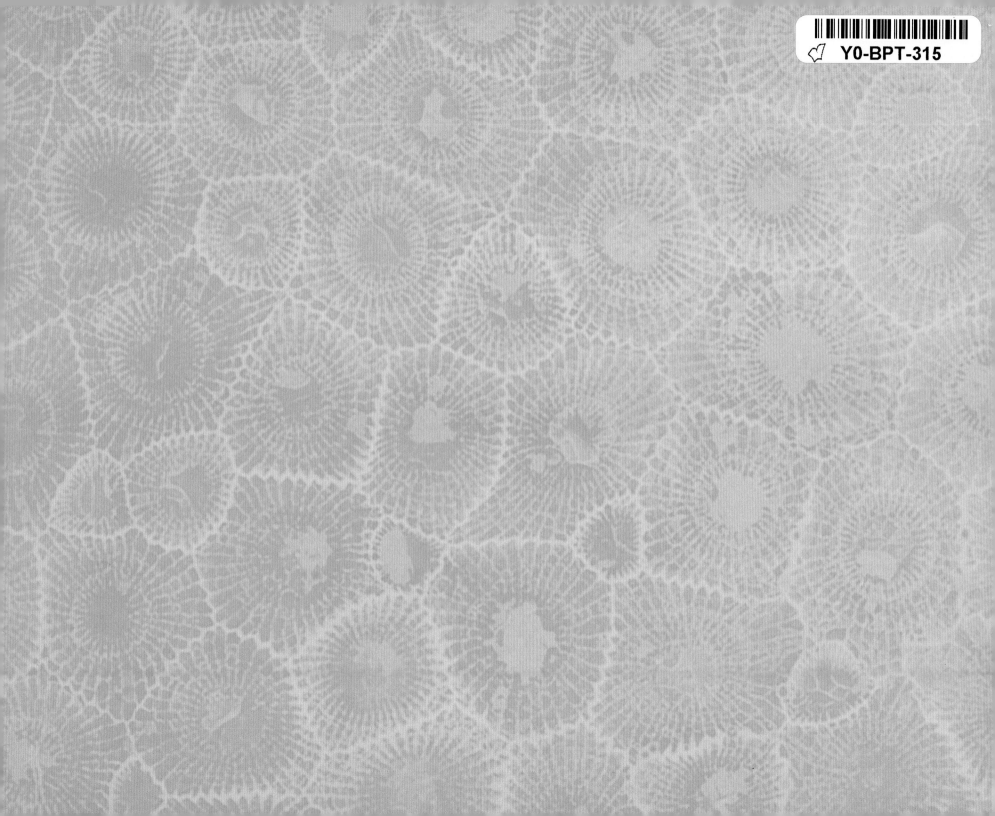

The PETOSKEY and ME

LOOK and FIND

C. M. BRENNER

SimplyCMB, LLC - Suttons Bay, MI

For my son.
You are my amazing.

Published by
simplyCMB, LLC, Suttons Bay, MI

Publisher's Cataloging-in-Publication Data
Brenner, C. M.

The Petoskey and me : look and find / C.M. Brenner. – Suttons Bay, MI : simplyCMB LLC, 2016.

p. ; cm.

ISBN13: 978-0-9980042-0-4

SUMMARY: A children's look and find activity book encouraging greater appreciation of nature and their own individuality.

1. Corals, Fossil--Michigan--Juvenile literature. 2. Natural resources conservation areas--Michigan, Lake--Juvenile literature. I. Title.

QE778.B74 2016
563.6—dc23   2015960193

Photographs by C. M. Brenner
Design by Yvonne Fetig Roehler

Printed in Malaysia by Tien Wah Press (PTE) Limited, First Printing, February 2016
20   19   18   17   16   •   5   4   3   2   1

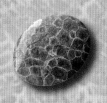

Hidden on each page is a Petoskey stone like this.
A northern Michigan treasure that can easily be missed.

As you're searching for the stone,
be sure to pause and see some of nature's beauty
I am blessed to have near me.

Then once you've found the many treasures shown inside this book,
get out and start exploring, and give your world a look.

The amazing secrets of nature are waiting to be discovered.
Treasures all around and in yourself to be uncovered.

Of all the beautiful nature
in northern Michigan to see,
there's a treasure you might miss
if you don't look carefully.

It's our state stone, the Petoskey stone, found near our northern shores.
A fossil with tiny sunburst rings from millions of years before.

A part of Michigan history and a beautiful design
have made the search for Petoskey stones a favorite northern pastime.

By the shore or on a dune
is where you'll likely find your keepsake,
but there are many other paths
that you can also take.

Petoskey stones can be found up here
most anywhere you go.
From fields and forests to rivers and roads,
some are in places we'll never know.

Our changing seasons uncover
and wash in fresh stones
the whole year through.
Wind and ice,
waves and rain
all help bring more in view.

Some Petoskey stones are easier to find than others.
When wet, their unique design stands out a great deal better.
But with patience, practice, and a good keen eye,
you'll eventually find some completely dry.

Do not be discouraged if the stones you find
have become rough and dull over seasons and time.
With a little water, the sunray pattern will be clearer.
Sand and polish more, and your Petoskey will shine like never before.

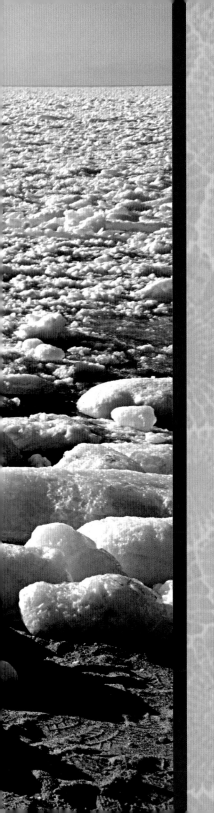

What makes Petoskey stones so fascinating to find?
After all, they're just rocks of a different fossil kind.

We love the search for them,
their history and design,
but they also hold a message
for you to keep in mind.

Many Petoskeys look like ordinary rocks
until a little polish brings their true beauty to the top.
You are like a Petoskey stone, precious and unique,
with the most special part of you often hidden just beneath.

Reveal what makes you special, be proud to let it show,
then remember to stay true to each special gift as you continue to grow.

Just as each Petoskey stone is different from the rest,
there is only one you, and being yourself is always best.

So get out and discover what is waiting for you in nature.
No doubt you will find it a most inspiring adventure.

Whether you live in northern Michigan or just visit for a time,
keep your eyes cast down, and a Petoskey you might find.
Then remember, it doesn't matter where you are or where you go,
you and you alone are the best treasure you can know.